THE GHOST *of* PEG-LEG PETER

and other stories of old New York

Other books by M. A. JAGENDORF

American Folklore Series:

NEW ENGLAND BEAN POT: Folktales of the New England States
UPSTATE, DOWNSTATE: Folktales of the Middle Atlantic States
SAND IN THE BAG: Folktales of Ohio, Indiana, and Illinois
THE MARVELOUS ADVENTURES OF JOHNNY DARLING (New York
   State)

European Folklore Series:

TYLL ULENSPIEGEL'S MERRY PRANKS (Flemish)
THE MERRY MEN OF GOTHAM (English)
THE PRICELESS CATS and Other Italian Folktales (Italy)
THE GYPSIES' FIDDLE and Other Gypsy Tales
   (*In collaboration with C. H. Tillhagen*)
IN THE DAYS OF THE HAN (from an ancient Chinese Folk Legend)
PIERRE PATELIN (from the Medieval French farce)
DOCTORS ALL (from the Spanish of Lope de Vega)

NOODLEHEAD STORIES FROM AROUND THE WORLD

KING OF THE MOUNTAINS: A Treasury of Latin-American Folk
   Stories
   (*In collaboration with R. S. Boggs*)

The GHOST of

and other stories of old New York

WITH ILLUSTRATIONS BY

& SONGS OF OLD NEW YORK

Peg-Leg Peter

M. A. JAGENDORF

Lino S. Lipinski

SELECTED BY JUNE LAZARE

THE VANGUARD PRESS, INC.
New York

to PEGEEN & EDWARD FITZGERALD

*In respect and admiration for their ceaseless aid
to creatures who cannot speak for themselves*

Foreword

It is interesting to note that many of the tales that have come down to us from olden days and are still currently told are great jests, hoaxes, and pranks in which folks used to take huge delight.

This is easy to understand if you keep in mind that in those days people had to fall back on themselves for amusement—one of the essential necessities of life.

Formerly there were none of the manufactured entertainment and pleasures that we have today. And so people consciously—or unconsciously—created them. Nimble minds were ever at work thinking up ideas and acts for a good laugh.

The stories in this book tell of these jests and hoaxes

and incidents of bygone life. A few of them, as you will read in the notes, are of folks and happenings within my memory and within the memory of some of my friends. But they have come into the realm of folklore by constant repetition from mouth to mouth and in writing. Of whatever period, they all were and still are good New York City fare, and I am sure you will enjoy them, even as young and old have enjoyed them through the years.

I want to express my thanks to the members of the Library of the New York Historical Society for their good help and to Miss C. S. Beresford in particular, who took no end of pains to dig up facts and books pertinent to the tales' authenticity.

I am also very grateful to Mr. Frank Schiffman, the director of the Apollo Theater in Harlem, who helped me so much with the "Hope Tree" tale.

M. JAGENDORF

New York City

Contents

Contents

The ardent, romantic, the charming God of song
Cross'd lately th' Atlantic, nor thought the voyage long,
He tripped along in shoes of cork, singing many a ditty,
But he chang'd his song when he reach'd New York
To What a Charming City

> *New York, New York, oh, what a charming city,*
> *New York, New York, oh, what a charming city.*

[From a song of old New York]

1   The tale of the three footsteps

Before the lands now called Westchester were taken over by white settlers, the Indians who lived there told of great arguments between the Devil and themselves. The Devil always screamed and shouted, "All the lands around these hills and rivers and meadows are mine and don't belong to you. Get out of my domain!"

The Indians danced a war dance, swung their tomahawks, strung their bows, and shouted back, "This is our land, these are our hunting grounds, and you have no right to be here. Get out, and get out fast, or our tomahawks will dance on your head and our arrows will make you look like a sieve for winnowing corn!"

Bad words flew all around like sparks from a burning log, and soon the stone clubs began to fly and the flint arrows began to whiz. Day after day the battle grew hotter. But the Indians were a whole tribe and the Devil was all alone. In the end the tomahawks and the arrows became too much for him and he had to flee.

He squatted down and dug his feet deep in the boulder on which he was standing. His right foot, which was his stronger foot, dug deeper than his left. He dug so hard he left a deep imprint of his right foot on the stone. Then he slowly rose up and took one giant leap, leaving the imprint of his foot far, far behind him.

He sailed through the air and landed on a big boulder near the place where Fort Schuyler was later built.

But the Indians were still after him. He heard their triumphant whooping and saw the arrows flying. So he thought it wiser to run farther away. Again he bent low, dug his right foot deep into the boulder on which he was standing—making a deep imprint on it—and took a great leap that landed him with a resounding thud on a big rock on the shore.

Then he rested for a time. He could still hear the Indian whoops coming near and the whizzing of their arrows. But he was at the water's edge, and the Devil did not like water. He looked to the right and he looked to the left. Big boulders jutted out of the water.

"I'll use them as steppingstones to get to the other side where the Indians can't follow me," he said to himself. He picked up his long tail, so as not to wet it, and began leaping from stone to stone. Then, with one giant leap, he landed on a huge boulder on the Long Island side, where he left the third mark of his right foot.

The Indian arrows and tomahawks could not reach him there. He took deep breaths, for he had been running hard.

The Indians chasing him came to the shore and there they performed a wild victory dance, leaping around and swinging their tomahawks high in the air.

The Devil watched them and became more furious every minute.

Then suddenly he leaped up again. He picked up the rocks and boulders lying all around him and one after the other began flinging them wildly across the water, across the Sound, into the land that is now Westchester and all the nearby parts. . . .

The Indians ran away, but the rocks remained on the land while the Devil remained peacefully on Long Island.

This is a true story, for to this day you can see the Devil's footprints in the rocks in Westchester and Fort

Schuyler and Long Island. And you can also see that there are very few rocks on the Island, while there are many in the land across the Sound. That's what Long Islanders say, and Long Islanders always tell true tales.

2 The ghost of Peg-Leg Peter

Peter Stuyvesant was governor of New Amsterdam when Manhattan Island belonged to the Dutch. The governor was often called "Silver Nails" because he had a wooden leg that had a silver band around it. He was proud of his wooden leg and of the town he ruled with a fearless hand.

It was a bitter day for him when he had to surrender New Amsterdam to the English fleet. But he still loved the city he had governed, which the English now called New York. So he decided to live there for the rest of his life, even though he hated the English more and more every day.

He lived peacefully and quietly on his farm, seeing just a few of his old Dutch friends. When he died, his

body was buried in a vault in a chapel he had built. That chapel and vault are still in New York City, alongside the Church of St. Mark's in the Bouwerie.

His body had been put into a closed vault. But that did not stop the ghost of the governor from stomping around on black or moonlit nights in his old haunts: his farm, and the city hall where he had once reigned. Folks heard his stomping peg leg with the silver band,

and saw him—and ran away in fear. That pleased him, particularly if they were English. He wanted no one around his grave, least of all the enemy who had robbed him and the Dutch Government.

What angered the governor's ghost most of all was the sight of the city creeping farther and farther north, all around his grave. He did not want his enemies near him, and he was all set to stop them. But the English settlers paid small heed to the ghost's wishes. They were now tampering with the graveyards around the church. Streets were spreading in all directions, wooden houses sprouting everywhere. Old "Silver Nails" was in ghostly fury. This running wild of the city had to stop!

Now the tappings and the bangings of the wooden leg were heard more often; the apparition in white lace ruffles and knickerbockers, a heavy stick in his hand, was seen more often. His hollow, haggard face looked wild and forbidding and black with anger at the killing of trees and the tearing up of earth. Workingmen, catching a glimpse of him, fled in terror.

But that did not stop the brutal work. If some men, afeard, would not return to their tasks, others took their place. So the work went on and on for a long time, the streets and houses growing all around. They were coming nearer and nearer to the governor's grave. Then . . . one day . . . workmen began cutting a road through the churchyard of Governor Stuyvesant's chapel. This was the moment when the ravaging must be stopped! The ghost governor decided to speak his anger so loud and fierce that the whole city would hear it. Those English bullies would not be permitted to destroy him in death even as they had destroyed him in life! Ghosts are not frightened by soldiers with cannons or men with shovels.

So one night the ghost came thumping out from the vault under the old trees and, going along the low bushes, came to the cobblestone path leading to the church door.

It happened, that night, that the sexton had come to the church to fetch some papers for the rector.

Stomp! Stomp! Stomp! The ghost came along the cobblestones. From the other direction hurriedly came the sexton.

The moon was only half full, but bright enough to show church, trees, and . . . ghost.

When the ghost saw the sexton, he raised his stick threateningly. The sexton raised his eyes, took one look, and ran off, screaming, "Help!"

The governor-ghost looked after the fleeing fellow with contempt and then stomped to the locked church door. He walked through it into the church and stomped up to the hanging bell rope. Taking it in his hands, he began pulling it savagely. And with every pull there was a wild clanging that could be heard near and far.

Folks heard the sexton's cries and the clamoring bell. They rushed out of their houses in night clothes, frightened and shouting, and ran to the church. The door was locked, but the piercing ringing screamed through the air, wilder than ever.

At last someone unlocked the door. The church was pitch black, but the bell was tolling frenziedly—its echo everywhere. Lanterns were lit. Not a soul was in sight, but the ringing was going on as if goblins and ghosts were clanging that clapper. Everyone stood petrified, unable to move. Then, suddenly, the ringing stopped.

They all rushed up to the rope—but there was only half a rope! It was torn high up in the middle; its lower part was gone.

The people were too frightened to speak. As they left the church, nobody said a word. The next morning the sexton found the other half of the torn rope—in Governor Stuyvesant's vault! Now everyone knew who had rung the bell. . . .

But the tearing up of woods and fields for roads, and the building of new houses went on just the same. Then Peter Stuyvesant's ghost knew he was beaten, just as he had known he was beaten when the great British fleet came sailing into the harbor to rob him of the city. . . .

Sometimes the ghost of the governor still comes out again and looks around sadly. But he never rings the bell any more, for he knows it will be of little use.

3 The courageous Quaker of Flushing

When folks from Jamaica and Flushing gather to talk of olden days, they like to tell the tale of John Bowne, the Quaker—John Bowne, who was a Quaker by choice and not by birth.

John Bowne came from England and went to live in Flushing Village, where an Englishman, Robert Hodgson, had settled with a group of Quakers to peaceful, honest work. The governors of New England had persecuted these peace-loving folk, and Peter Stuyvesant, governor of New Amsterdam, did the same.

John Bowne had met Hannah, a fine girl and a Quaker, and the two had married and lived in Flushing where they had a farm. John was a hard worker and a fearless man, the kind the new country needed.

One day he was traveling with a friend to the next village. They were going through the brambly woods when suddenly a huge brown bear came toward them.

High on his hind legs, his jaws wide open, he looked like a frightening giant. He was heading straight for the two men.

Because he was a Quaker, John's friend carried no weapons, and John had only a heavy branch in his hand that he used as a walking stick.

As the bear came toward them with blood-red eyes, ready to tear them to pieces, Bowne raised his thick stick and thrust it deep against the beast's throat, holding it there until the bear fell down and they could go on their way.

Sometimes John went with his wife Hannah to the "Friends' meetings" on Sundays. That was what the Quakers called their services, which, like everything in their lives, they tried to keep very simple. John liked their honest ways of life and worship and soon joined the "Society."

By then, John, with hard work, had built for himself and his wife a fine farmhouse, and when the Friends had no place to hold their meetings, he offered his house for their worship.

Now, offering a home for worship to the Quakers was forbidden by law.

Governor Stuyvesant had passed harsh laws against the "abominable" sect, as he called the Quakers—"the abominable sect who treat with contempt the political

magistrates and the ministers of God's Holy Word"
—and he carried out these laws ruthlessly.

The governor knew of Bowne and his fearless opposi-
tion to his decrees. He was determined to punish him
and to set him up as an example for the colony.

Whenever the two met there were harsh words between them, the hotheaded governor upbraiding Bowne
and threatening him, and the soft-spoken Bowne saying
he behaved according to the laws of God and man and
that bad laws made by man should be stricken off the
records.

When the freeholders of Flushing and neighboring
towns petitioned the governor to rescind the unfair
laws, the governor was infuriated beyond words and he
decided to act according to his authority. The signers of
the petition were punished—but a greater example was
to be made of John Bowne: The governor sent out soldiers to Flushing to arrest him.

When the soldiers came to John Bowne's home to
carry out the arrest, he demanded to know the reason.

"What laws have I broken?" he asked.

The officer took out his warrant and read it to him:

"Harboring men of your abominable sect who treat
with contempt the political magistrates and the ministers of God's Holy Word and endeavor to undermine
the police and religion."

"These are hard and cruel and unjust laws and should
not be on our books," John Bowne replied.

Just the same, he was taken to prison. He was tried
and condemned to pay twenty-five Flemish pounds.

When he refused, the governor ordered him banished from the colony on the first ship ready to sail.

Folks tried again and again to soften the heart of the governor, but it was of no avail. Bowne languished in prison for one long year, and finally, in 1663, he was sent back to Holland on the *Guilded Fox*.

The journey was long and hard, and as an exile Bowne was not treated too gently. But he never lost his courage; he was not a man to be frightened or disheartened by difficulties.

No sooner had he set foot on ground than he went to "manifest" his case before the West India Company of Amsterdam.

He spoke quietly and simply and in measured words to these men in dark clothes with big clean white collars, laying his case before them. He finished with the words: "My conscience is free and unshackled and I know it will remain so all my life."

The good Hollanders listened to him with deep attention, measuring his words with the accuracy with which they measured their diamonds.

These men believed in fairness, and they had the welfare of the colony at heart. They took their time and deliberated, considering the case carefully. They concluded that John Bowne had done nothing against the good of the colony and that no bad word should be spoken against him. Nor did they approve of Governor Stuyvesant's persecution of Bowne because of his religion. They wanted every man to remain free so long as he was modest and moderate and did not offend others or oppose the government. They wanted all rigorous proceedings against the Quakers to cease.

They sent Bowne back to the new land. They also sent back a strong letter to the governor, urging him to use wisdom and forbearance or they would destroy the colony.

Though Governor Stuyvesant was hotheaded and hard-tempered, he was also wise and understanding. From then on he stopped persecuting the Quakers, and they lived peacefully with their neighbors.

That is why Flushing folks, Quakers and others, like to tell the tale of John Bowne, a man of courage and of peace.

4 How the Duyvil gave New Amsterdam to the English

Nearly everything in the world has two ends, and so has New York City's Manhattan Island. This tale happened at both ends of the island. It started at the southern, lower end and finishes at the northern, upper end.

In the olden, golden days, Manhattan was called New Amsterdam. The Dutch settlers bought the island from the Indians for sixty guilders, which at the time was worth twenty-four dollars, and named it after their famous city in Holland. In the Dutch days the city's population was concentrated at the lower end of the island. Beyond the city were hills and woods with many little villages; on one side of the island was the gleaming Hudson River, on the other side, the sparkling East River.

New Amsterdam was ruled by governors. The mightiest of them all was Peter Stuyvesant, who had a wooden leg and was a great warrior. Next to him in fame was Anthony the Trumpeter. Anthony was big and fat, with long whiskers and a large broad nose that shone like polished copper in a Dutch kitchen. He could hold his breath longer and blow out his breath stronger than any "Dutchman" in New Amsterdam. For that reason Governor Peter Stuyvesant made him the trumpeter of his army and of all the colony. Anthony was very proud of this honor and blew his trumpet all the time.

When he blew the trumpet it was louder than Joshua's trumpet that toppled the walls of Jericho. Whenever the Indians came to battle the Dutch for the wrongs they had committed against them, Anthony would blow his trumpet so loud that it put the Indians to flight.

One day the peg-legged governor heard that the English fleet was coming to attack him and take his city for their British ruler.

The governor called Anthony to his council chamber.

"Anthony," he roared sternly, "cease dallying with your Dutch sweethearts and come to the rescue of your country. The thieving robbers, the English pirates, are coming with their ships to steal the city from our crown. Go out into the villages on the island and the villages along the Hudson River and blow your trumpet stronger than you've ever blown it before. Summon all good burghers to come and help defeat the British scoundrels."

"I am going," Anthony replied, "and I'll blow my trumpet loud enough to be heard in the other world. Trust me, Governor Stuyvesant. We'll beat those ruffians so they'll run away like curs with tails between their legs."

Anthony bade farewell to the many Dutch girls with whom he had been friendly and set out, his gilded trumpet hanging on one side of his doublet and his large, heavy stone jug on the other.

It was a windy, stormy day, but Anthony went on valiantly. From time to time he would take a hearty sip from his trusty stone jug and would blow his trusty trumpet. So, toward night, he came to the northern end of the island. To get to the other side of the land, he had to cross water. He hallooed for the ferryman, but no

ferryman came with any boat. He stormed up and down, he shouted, he even blew his mighty trumpet, but only the blasting wind roared back at him. No ferryman came.

He looked at the choppy waves and took a deep draught from his trusty jug.

"Ha!" he roared, "I'll cross that water *en spuyt den Duyvil* [in spite of the Devil]!" The words were said and the deed was done.

He plunged into the churning cold water, his gleaming trumpet held high in one hand and his trusty jug in the other. With mighty strength of arm and legs he moved forward. But the Duyvil deep down in the Hudson River had heard Anthony's brash boast. Swiftly he came up from the muddy bottom and there he was, looking fiercely at the breasting trumpeter.

The Devil had taken the form of a giant green fish with a huge tail slashing out of the water and raising the waves hill-high. The devil-fish opened his mouth wide enough to swallow ten men in one gulp, and out came a fierce roar. He was steering straight for Anthony.

"Ha, so you think you can spite me! You yoicking, red-nosed minnow, squeaking puny squeaks on your tin trumpet! I'll teach you to dare me!" he bellowed.

He lashed his long tail fiercely in the leaping water.

"I'll show you how to spite me!" he screamed into the wind, and he got hold of Anthony's leg.

The fearless trumpeter brought the trumpet to his lips and let out a blast in the howling gale so fierce that

it frightened even the wind. For one moment even the devil-fish let go of Anthony's leg. But he quickly got hold of it again and began pulling the trumpeter down . . . down . . . down . . . deep.

Anthony fought heroically, his fiery nose becoming redder and redder in the dark, stormy night, but he was going down, down . . . deeper . . . deeper. . . . Soon there was just a faint gleam of his nose through the black water.

The storm roared wild and the water leaped high, but Anthony wasn't there any more. . . .

That was the reason he did not blow his trumpet that would have roused the Dutch burghers to come to the rescue of fair New Amsterdam. And that was why the English conquered New Amsterdam and called it New York.

But on stormy nights, folks who live on the upper end of Manhattan say they can hear Anthony's blowing trumpet in the roaring winds. For though the Devil conquered Anthony's body, he could never conquer his blowing trumpet. And to this day the place is called "Spuyten Duyvil."

5 Clever Mistress Murray

When fine ladies who live today in the Murray Hill section of New York City speak of fine ladies who lived there in the olden days, they mention first Mrs. Robert Murray. Her husband was one of the richest merchants in New York in the days of Washington and they had a beautiful summer home at what is now Fifth Avenue and Thirty-seventh Street. Today the entire section is named after the Murrays, but folks did not call it the Murray Hill section in the olden days.

Mr. Murray was a very clever Quaker merchant, and Mrs. Murray was a very clever lady, with a quick wit and a quick mind. There was one giant disagreement between them. Mr. Murray believed in the British cause, and Mrs. Murray and her beautiful daughters were heart and soul with the men who were fighting to make America independent. And so men from both sides visited their lovely country home.

Came the day when the British landed in Kips Bay, which is on the east side of Manhattan, to capture General Washington and his army. The British outnumbered the Americans and so the Americans were in retreat. All but four thousand men, under the command of General Putnam, had gotten well away on the Bloomingdale Road. Now the Americans needed time to move the rest.

That very day, General Washington was visiting Mistress Murray and her lovely daughters at their summer home. Master Murray was away on a business journey, and the general was being entertained graciously by Mistress Murray and her daughters. They were talking of the war.

"The British are on the march," said Mistress Murray.

"I know that well, madame. But we'll escape and we'll win. At the moment we need just a few more hours. Old Putnam and his men are hard on the march to join the army that's up on the shores of the Hudson River. When he joins them, all will be safe."

"True indeed, General. Thee knowest well, he who fights and retreats a way, lives to fight another day." They all laughed.

"Well said, Mistress Murray, and I thank you from my very heart for a few happy and restful hours. Now I must be off to my men. You can hear the thunder of the cannons."

They all said good-by and good luck, and off went the general and two officers on their horses over the hills and heights.

The British were indeed on the march, headed by General William Howe and his officers. These men were ahead of their troops and were approaching the home of the Murrays. General Howe and Master Robert Murray were staunch friends, and so the British general decided to stop off for a little time at the Murrays' home.

Mistress Murray and her beautiful daughters were out listening to the sound of the approaching troops. Suddenly in the distance they saw a group of brightly dressed officers approaching.

"They are coming this way, Mother."

"Yes, methinks it is General Howe and his staff. Daughters, we must do our best to keep General Howe here as long as possible to let General Putnam and his men escape. Remember, General Washington said he needs a few more hours."

"We will do our best—here they are, Mother."

And so they all went out on the green, sweet smiles of welcome on their lips.

Soon the British general and a large number of his staff rode up on prancing horses.

"Good day to you, beautiful Mistress Murray, and to your lovely daughters," said General Howe, his uniform gleaming.

"Welcome to our home, General. Thee and thy officers must alight and refresh yourselves awhile. There is good cake and repast and you must taste the wines my daughters and I have made from berries. I have just brought up some five-year-old mulberry wine. It is delicious. And we also have good Madeira from England."

"Nothing will give me greater pleasure. A happy hour with you, Mistress, will shorten a whole week's hard work."

The general and his officers dismounted from their horses, which were taken away by the servants.

General Howe continued: "I'll get that ragtail, bobtail mob that calls itself an army and their misguided officers when I'm ready. For the present, it will be a great joy to be in the charming company of such lovely ladies."

The girls curtsied and smiled winningly at the redcoated officers with their glistening sabers.

"Sir," said the eldest of the girls, "I helped Mother

make the mulberry wine—it is truly delicious. And you must try the fine Madeira of which Mother spoke."

The table was richly set with fine cakes and dainties; decanters gleamed with golden yellow and dark ruby wines. Howe and his officers forgot all about battles and soldiers, even though they could hear now and then the cannons thundering. They ate freely and drank deeply and discussed the fire that had just swept through the city.

Well fed, richly entertained by good conversation, the hours went by; finally the men slowly began to get ready to leave.

"We must keep them longer," Mistress Murray whispered to her eldest daughter.

The girl just closed her eyes, meaning "yes." She got up.

The Murrays had an unusually beautiful young serving girl, and Mistress Murray had noticed that the younger officers had paid considerable attention to her.

"Gentlemen," said Mistress Murray gaily, "I know it's time to go, but what is a fine repast without a fine song? Young Daisy, my little maid, besides being so pretty—I noticed some of you young gentlemen looking at her kindly—has a charming voice."

"Yes, and we have just received some tuneful songs from London," said the oldest daughter. "Why not have her sing for us?"

"Aye, come gentlemen, just a little longer. You must listen to Daisy's singing," said Mistress Murray.

"I'll fetch more mulberry wine and more cold meats and cakes. These should go well with the songs," said the youngest daughter.

The men felt warm and happy and were only too glad to stay. Daisy sang "Sally in Our Alley" and many other songs, and the men drank more while the fingers on the clock moved steadily.

Finally a reluctant parting had to come, and the men went out to mount their horses. Mistress Murray and her daughters were on the steps. The roaring of the cannons had died down and there was no more smoke in the blue air.

A young officer came dashing up to the mounting officers.

"Sir," he spoke quickly to General Howe, "sir, the rebels have escaped through McGowan's Pass. All of 'em, with their leader, Putnam. . . . Perhaps if we had left early . . ."

General Howe was too comfortable with food and wine to be bothered.

"Young man, the fine feast and good wines and the entertainment served by these lovely loyal ladies are of much greater importance than that riffraff mob of rebels. We can catch them any time. We don't find such entertainment every day. Thank you, lovely Mistress and lovely girls, and you, sweet little Daisy."

The officers joined in the thanks and the red-coated officers rode away.

Mistress Murray stood on the steps, radiant and smiling. Her daughters, their faces flushed and their eyes shining, stood with her.

"The entertainment was successful indeed," said Mistress Murray. "General Putnam and his four thousand men had plenty of time to join General Washington's army up the Hudson. 'He who fights and retreats a way, lives to fight another day.'" Her daughters smiled knowingly.

That is why, to this very day, fine ladies who live in the Murray Hill section mention Mrs. Murray first when speaking of the fine ladies of the olden days who lived there.

6 The phantom fire ship

The waters called the Sound round Long Island run in and out of the land like crazy curlicues. In the olden days they were a haven for buccaneers and pirates, who were the rulers of the sea. Fishers Island, Gardiners Island, and all such other islands, Hallets Cove and all the other coves, were fine hiding places for these marauders, who were ready to rob, destroy, and run. And sad to say, as often as not rich merchants and officers of the law were partners of these robbers and shielded them from honest prosecution.

Governor Peter Stuyvesant had a hard time keeping the waters safe for merchants and sailing vessels. He issued a decree for safety. Forty men were levied to watch the waters day and night. They were to give an alarm when they sighted a pirate ship, and so save vessels and goods. Eight men were assigned to Manhattan and the rest to the villages all over Long Island: Breuckelen (Brooklyn), Flushing, Jamaica, and others farther out. Day and night these watchmen were on the lookout for any suspicious vessel that appeared on the horizon. But watching did not help too much. The human sharks roamed up and down, hid when pursued, and made life on the sea hard.

One sunny day a good ship set out from Pelham Bay with a rich cargo of furs, some passengers, and a white horse to be delivered at one of the harbors on the way.

The wind danced properly for sails, white shells of foam tossed over the swells, and everyone was in good spirits. The horse was neighing in the wind, nostrils distended, and the wavelets were lapping against the ship's painted hull.

The wind blew high, the wind blew low, and the ship glided under an easy sail. The crew worked with a good will and the passengers sat around on bales and barrels, never dreaming of harm. But the captain kept watch with an eagle eye, for he knew that pirates and buccaneers might be lurking everywhere; one could not be too wary.

So the day passed on and the sun was going down in a bed of golden sheen when the captain and the mate on lookout saw a sailing vessel coming toward them. Both men looked with knitted brows and soon their suspicions proved true.

The men were ordered to arm, while the passengers stood about, too terrified to move.

The vessel came so near, you could see its armed crew on deck. Then came a roar: "Surrender!"

But the captain was not the kind to give up.

"Up with the white flag and surrender!" again came the roar across the water.

A well-aimed shot was the captain's answer. The pirate ship came abreast, grappling hooks were thrown over the rail, and her wild crew swarmed aboard.

The seamen put up a valiant defense, but the bloodthirsty pirate crew ran up and down like wild beasts on the hunt, sparing no one, forgetting man and God.

Quickly they removed the cargo, even down to the passengers' rings, and just as quickly boarded their own ship.

"Take off!" the captain yelled to his crew. "But first, let's light their way. Tie the horse to the mast and set the ship on fire!" With a mean laugh he lit some litter lying near him.

The horse was promptly put aboard and the ship was set on fire at different places. The wild pirate crew departed in their own craft to sail their sinful way, leaving the burning vessel behind them with nothing alive on it but the white horse.

The vessel burned and burned and the horse screamed with nearly a human voice. But there was none to hear him except the water and the flames.

Then the strangest thing that ever happened on Long Island Sound happened on that ship!

It burned and it burned and it burned! And it kept on burning like the burning bush in the Bible that did not burn to ashes.

The flames gave no smoke and did not destroy. They just leaped around and all over the ship. All over the sails and all over the rigging, heating all to red, red heat. And when the flames leaped around the crew or passengers . . . it burned life into them!

Wounds closed, men rose, and all began going about their tasks as if nothing had happened. The sailors climbed rigging red as molten iron and pulled red-burning ropes.

The blistering, blazing flames seemed to give strength to life instead of turning it into ashes.

But no one spoke a word. The only sounds were the crackling of the flames, the whistling of the wind in the flaming sails, and the slapping of the waves running away from the boat. No sound came from the burning lips of crew and passengers; only the horse was neighing as he pawed the burning wood. Never was there a ghostly ship alight with such harmless golden flames!

The red-roaring ship dipped down, rose up, and sailed in a careening, crazy way. The crew and passengers on the fiery craft went about the scorching silence, not even taking note of one another. The big white horse tied to the thick, thick foremast kept on neighing all the time, sparks flying from its hoofs as it pawed the flame-covered deck. Thus the burning ship-banner of horror followed the terror-stricken pirate ship in wild flight, lumbering and zigzagging, a fierce horror to see.

Some of the pirate crew even crossed themselves and began to pray—something they had not done in years. But it made no difference to the burning phantom ship —it was ever following them.

The pirate ship fled on, steering madly to escape. Finally it slipped into one of the hundreds of hidden coves that are found up and down Long Island Sound: along Little Neck Bay, Hempstead Harbor, East Chester Bay—everywhere along the narrow land.

The pirate ship escaped, but the phantom fire ship continued sailing around the islands and inlets and coves of Long Island Sound.

On stormy nights, when wild northwesters rage over the churning seas, the golden burning craft, like a giant star, bobs and lurches and glides and leaps along the water while the waves rush away from the burning wood as if in fearful terror.

The crew work on the burning deck and sails and rigging and the passengers walk about in a furnace-hot silence, while the big white horse neighs fiercely with near a human voice!

Many out on boats on such fearful nights, near the shore or around Pelham Bay, Little Neck Bay, Manhasset, Hempstead Harbor, Echo Bay, and other places from Hell Gate to Gardiners Island, have seen that frightful gleaming sight.

That's what folks tell you who live in those places and sail around Long Island Sound, and I am telling it to you.

7   Commodore Vanderbilt's first boat

Cornelius Vanderbilt's father was a seventh son. That should have made him wise and lucky. But he was not wise or lucky, and his family would have been in sad straits if not for his wife Phebe. Phebe was a smart and thrifty *huisvrouw* and kept home and children in food and order.

She had many children, and one of them was Cornelius the younger. He looked like his father, big and tall, with blue eyes and flaxen hair, but he was as smart as his mother and full of ambition.

He was a strong boy and he liked to work. When he was only six he was already earning money by doing small jobs around neighbors' houses and at the waterfront. Whatever he earned he gave to his mother, and she put it away in the big brown grandfather's clock that stood against the wall.

Of all the children, Corneel, as he was sometimes called, was the smartest and the hardest-working. He was forever wanting to do more and more—bigger and better jobs to earn more money so that his mother would not have to work so hard. Phebe and Corneel were close to each other. But Cornelius and his father did not get along too well.

Father Cornelius Vanderbilt owned a piragua—that is, a flat-bottomed boat with two masts used for ferrying and hauling. Young Corneel soon could run it. He wanted to start working before the sun was up, but his father Cornelius said that was too early and folks were still asleep. Young Corneel wanted to work late at night, but father Cornelius said that night was the time for staying home with your family. So these two were at odds and would often get into quarrels. Then the mother would step in to bring peace between them. But it was only an outward peace for young Corneel. In his heart the boy was dissatisfied and unhappy.

When Corneel was sixteen he was as big and strong as any man and could work better than many. He felt he was a man now, and did not want to work with his father, who was too slow for him. Why not enlist as a sailor on a ship and sail off to far lands? Many a boy had done that.

He thought about this day and night—but there was his mother! She worked hard. His father did not earn enough and Corneel felt he had to help. What would happen if he went away? Phebe needed her son to help keep the house going. But on the sea there was adventure, and maybe he could earn more money than on land. He was torn between desire and duty.

In the end he decided to go, but he would tell his mother first.

One evening, after the others had gone to bed, he told her what he planned to do. She listened to him patiently, for she understood her son's feelings.

"I know how you feel, son. Young eagles get tired of their nests. I know you and your father don't get along very well, but he is well-meaning and he loves you and he has worked hard for many years to bring you up."

"I know, Mother, but he is always telling me what to do when I know it can be done better. I know I'll do better when I am away from him. There's good money for seamen."

"You can't leave us, Bub; we can't do without you."

"Then I want to work for myself. If only I had a boat of my own, I'd be glad to stay. I'd show you how I could make money so we wouldn't always be worrying and wanting. If only I had a hundred dollars—I know where I could get a fine piragua for that right now. She's in Port Richmond, right here on Staten Island! She could hold a dozen passengers and I'd make big money with her."

"A hundred dollars is a lot of money, son."

"I know, Mother. If only I could borrow it!"

For a few minutes the dark room was silent, then Phebe spoke slowly:

"A hundred dollars is a lot of money, but let me talk it over with your father and hear what he says."

"I know what he'll say. He'll say no. He always says no to everything I want."

Phebe looked at her son; then she said, "Wait for the morrow, Corneel son. Wait till I have spoken to your father."

No one has ever told whether Phebe spoke to her husband or not, but early the next morning Phebe said to her son:

"Corneel, I'll lend you a hundred dollars for the piragua—but there is a condition."

Young Cornelius looked at his mother: "What is the condition, Mother?"

"You know the eight-acre piece of land we have in Port Richmond?"

"Yes, Mother."

"Well, if you clear the rocks, plow it up, and harrow it and seed it with corn by your birthday—the twenty-seventh of this month—I'll lend you the money for the piragua." She looked straight at Cornelius, and he knew from her look that she meant every word.

Those eight acres of land were full of stones and hadn't been touched by a plow ever. It was a hard task, one that would take a few men two or three weeks to do. And it was just *three* weeks to his birthday!

For a time there was silence in the room. Cornelius looked down at the floor. He knew it was a hard undertaking. His eyebrows were wrinkled and he thought hard. Suddenly he straightened up. With his quick mind he had hit on a way of doing that near-impossible job.

"Mother, I'll do it. I'll clear that piece of land, plow it, harrow it, and seed it by my birthday."

Phebe Vanderbilt smiled. She knew her son would do it.

He left the room. Already his plan was laid out. He began looking for his friends, and soon had quite a few around him.

"How would you like riding in a piragua with me, just for fun?"

There was a chorus of answers and all were the same:

"We sure would."

"Well, give me a hand clearing a field, plowing, harrowing, and seeding it, and I'll have a piragua of my own to use in three weeks."

These boys were used to farmwork and they all promised to help. No fourteen- to sixteen-year-old boy had a boat of his own—here was a chance to share one.

They all went to work with enthusiasm, excitement, and good will. When a job is fun and pleasure, it goes fast.

They and Cornelius dug away, cleared, and sweated every minute they had free. Hours did not count. They stopped only when they had to. The stones were set in piles for fences. Soon the plowing was done . . . the harrowing . . . then the corn seeding. . . . Every boy was proud of the work.

It was the afternoon before young Cornelius' birthday. The boy was alone in the field putting in the last corn seed. When the final kernel was in, he straightened up and began racing home. Only his mother was there, standing over the stove. His face was flushed and excited and he could hardly speak clearly.

"Mother, the field is cleared, plowed, harrowed, and seeded, and tomorrow is my birthday. Remember your promise."

Phebe looked at her son, and there was pride in her eyes.

"I know you did it, son; I watched you. I didn't think you could, but you were smarter than I was and got ahead of me. I'll lend you the money. See that you make good use of it."

"Thanks, Mother! I'll show you I'll make good use of it!"

Phebe went to the old brown grandfather clock, opened its door, and took out a small bag. From it she slowly counted out the hundred dollars.

"Here, son, you deserve it."

Cornelius took the money and stammered out his thanks. Then he was out of the house, racing wildly to where the boat was for sale. Its owner was sitting on the dock, feet dangling over the water, smoking a pipe.

"I have the money here to buy your boat!" Cornelius shouted, all out of breath.

"You are young Corneel, aren't you?"

"That I am and I have a hundred dollars for your boat. You said it was for sale."

"That's right. Count out your money and I'll make

out the paper for you. I know your good parents. They're fine folks."

The man took the money and made out the paper: young Cornelius Vanderbilt was the proud owner of the boat.

That afternoon and the next day there was as much rejoicing among the boys who had helped as there was on the part of Cornelius.

They were sailing along the sparkling bay with a brisk wind, happy as gulls. They talked of sailing every day, but Corneel didn't say anything—these boys didn't know young Cornelius Vanderbilt. He had other plans.

Early the next morning Corneel was at the dock with his boat, telling one and all he was ready to sail anyone who wished to cross to Manhattan for eighteen cents, or there and back for twenty-five cents. He was also ready to carry freight or produce anyplace.

When his friends spoke of going out sailing for fun, his answer was: "That's for holidays and when I have the time. Now it's work."

Customers came fast, and Corneel worked like a boy of sixteen who is full of ambition would work.

Day after day he was in his boat ferrying and carrying. Folks quickly learned they could depend on him. His trade got bigger and bigger and he beat many a grown man who was doing the same kind of work. Pennies became dollars. And the more he earned, the harder he worked. Long and steady hours were his way, and he grew stronger and richer by the day.

On his seventeenth birthday, a year after he had bought the boat, he came home early. His mother was working as usual.

"Mother," he said, "a year ago you loaned me a hundred dollars to buy the piragua. Here is the money," and he proudly handed her a hundred dollars. "And, Mother, I told you I would make much money. Here is a thousand dollars more. I earned it honestly—no smuggling or anything crooked. The money'll keep you from working so hard. You helped me, now I am ready to help you."

Phebe Vanderbilt was silent for a long time. She looked at her son with shining, tearful eyes. Cornelius Vanderbilt, the father, who was at home, was silent too. Then they both thanked young Cornelius happily.

In later life Corneel became Commodore Cornelius Vanderbilt. He worked hard and earned much money.

He bought more and more boats, and with the years he became very famous and one of the richest men in our land. But he loved to tell his friends the tale of his first boat, and so the story is still told today.

"Mornin', Mighty Mose"

There are a hundred tales about Mighty Mose and he is worth many hundreds more. Even just talking about his daily doings is a fine tale full of excitement and adventure. So I'll tell you about a morning stroll of the strongest man who ever lived in New York City.

Here's what he looked like, so you will know him a little better.

He was the tallest man in New York City, a little over eight feet, and he had the biggest feet in all the city. His shoes, which needed two shoemakers to make them, had copper soles with inch-long nails. His arms and hands were so long they hung below his knees. He had flaming red hair. That's the kind of man Mose was.

His best friend was little Syksee, who followed him

like a shadow and worshiped him as if he were a shrine.

"He's the biggest, strongest man in all America," Syksee boasted, and the fire brigade of engine "Lady Washington No. 40" thought the same.

Every morning Syksee met his hero, Mighty Mose, when Mose went to take his little walk.

One morning the two met in Paradise Square. Mose carried a ten-foot hickory wagon tongue for a walking cane, and he puffed on a two-foot cigar, making clouds of smoke.

"Mornin', Mighty Mose."

"Mornin', Syksee. I'm gonna take a little swim across the Hudson twenty times an' that'll give me a good appetite."

The two of them trotted to the Hudson River and there Mighty Mose took the cigar out of his mouth, laid his walking stick down on the grass, took off some of his clothes, and dived in, holding his cigar high over his head.

Now, it took Big Mose only two good breast strokes to swim across the wide Hudson River. After taking one giant stroke under the water, he reached the middle of the river. There he raised his head for breath and saw in front of him a great British sailing ship sailing in his way.

His eyes flashed fire. Who dared to block the way of Mighty Mose? He raised his voice—and when that giant of New York City raised his voice, it was like a fall hurricane roaring along the southern oceans.

"Out of my way with your leaky tub," he bellowed.

The captain stood on the bridge and saw the giant redhead yowling at him out of the gray-blue water, but he wasn't the least scared.

"My vessel will sail along whether you like it or not, and it isn't leaky, either," he screamed back.

"Get it out of my way, an' do it quick. I'm gonna swim across the Hudson twenty times an' your rickety tub with the flapping rags is in my way. If you don't get out of the way, I'll send you down where the dead shads lie."

"I'd like to see you do it," screamed the fearless captain.

"You wanna see me do it, eh!" roared Mighty Mose. "I'll show you!"

With one sweep he turned around and with one stroke he was back on shore.

"Watch, Syksee, we're gonna have a little sport. I'll teach that Englishman to keep his boat out of my way when I take my swim across the Hudson. I'll make him dance till he crawls on his knees and begs for mercy," and Mighty Mose roared with laughter. The houses shook, the trees bent to the ground, and a gale danced wildly through New York City.

"Show 'm, fix 'm, Mose!" Syksee screamed.

Mose put his cigar in his mouth and, holding his head high so as not to get his weed wet, leaped into the water. He took one stroke and was in the middle of the Hudson not far from the British sailing ship. Then he took a deep, deep puff on his cigar and, with a powerful, powerful breath, let out billows and billows of gray smoke that went smack against the sails of the British sailing ship.

The great ship took a leap like a flying dolphin out of the sea and then plumped splashing back into the water.

"Now you'll get out of my way and let me take my morning swim," shrieked Mose between his teeth. Then he took another puff on his cigar and again blew it hard at the sails. The boat leaped again, careened around and nearly turned a somersault, and crashed back into the water.

"Ha! you worm of a captain with the brains of a flea, will you keep out of my way when I want to take my morning swim?"

The captain and the crew were tumbling about on that ship like pebbles in a pan.

"Please, sir Captain, give in quick before we drown or are smashed to bits," the crew pleaded.

The captain was a fearless man, but he saw that he had met one stronger than he was and that capitulation was wiser than stubbornness.

"I'll get out of your way—just stop blowing at my ship. I'll put in at a dock till your swim is finished," he shouted.

"That's the way to talk to Big Mose of New York City," said Mose, and he turned toward shore to save his good cigar.

The ship docked and Mighty Mose took his morning exercise, swimming twenty times back and forth across the lordly Hudson. And he did it in just forty strokes.

Then the "big Bowery b'hoy," as he and his kind were called in New York City in those days, went to have his breakfast with little Syksee.

"That's the way to start the day just right—without being bothered by English flies called sailing vessels messin' up our Hudson River," said Mighty Mose of the Empire City.

9 The bloodless battle of the elm

New York City had grown like mushrooms in a field where cows and horses pasture. It had become one of the world's large seaports. From the Battery up, streets and houses and streets and houses had spread on all sides. The city had gone far north of Canal Street. Then the city planners decided to lay out plans of streets for all the island of Manhattan. These streets would be named with hard numbers easy to remember, not lovely names pleasant to hear.

So houses had sprung up farther and farther north until they reached what is now Tenth Street, where Mynheer Hendrick Brevoort's *bouwerie* (or farm) lay peaceful and rich. It was a big farm, with great meadows and brooks, and Mynheer Brevoort was proud of it. He did not like to see the two main streets of the city, the Bowery and Broadway, coming closer and closer to him.

His father had lived on the same farm in peace, and he wanted to spend his years there too—in peace. He loved his red and black tiled house, the lower part of which was an inn for just a few old guests: men his own age, and Hendrick was ninety-four.

It was pleasant to sit there with friends and guests, all of them smoking their pipes and talking.

He loved his garden, with its pears and apples and strawberries. It was cool and restful to walk in the shade of his big maples and elms and tulip trees. Now he heard that a street had been planned *right through his bouwerie!* It was to go farther uptown and to straighten out the Bowery and Broadway so that they would run parallel to each other.

Ruin his bouwerie! Bring dust and dirt and noise into his home! Destroy all the good things of his life!

No, that must never happen! He was altogether against these crazy, new-fangled ideas. He wanted his oldtime peace and pleasure!

"While I live, no one will touch my bouwerie—no commissioners can pay me for it. I don't need their money," old Hendrick Brevoort said grimly.

He was sitting that evening with his friend Jacob Ruisdal, who had a farm not far away. Both were smoking their clay pipes, and before them stood a jug of fine pear wine Hendrick had brought from his cellar.

"Jacob," Hendrick said, "the city of New Amsterdam

was good enough for my forefathers, and even though it is now called New York, I want it as it was in their days. The city is getting too big for quiet living. It's spreading too far, with all kinds of riffraff coming in."

"You never said a word more true, Hendrick."

"I'll tell you one thing, Jacob: They'll never tear my bouwerie in two to please their crazy commission, and they won't touch a tree of mine either."

"How can you stop them? It is an order from City Hall."

"You just wait and see, friend Jacob. You just wait and see. They must ask my permission first." There was a fierce glint in his dark-gray eyes.

"You must not do anything, Hendrick, that will get you into trouble with the authorities."

"This is my land and I am the authority here! I inherited this land from my father and no one can take even a part of it from me without my permission. No road will go through it."

"But if the government orders you . . ."

"The government can't tell me what to do with my own land. No road will go through it. There's plenty of land all around they can use."

Just the same, four days later four surveyors and engineers came working up along meadows and fields toward the farm of Hendrick Brevoort. They wore big boots and carried all kinds of lines and staves to mark off the trees to indicate where the roads and streets were to run.

Slowly they worked their way toward Hendrick Brevoort's home.

It was early afternoon. The inn was empty and Hendrick was sitting on the porch reading the Good Book with a magnifying glass, never dreaming the enemy was on the way.

Suddenly he was interrupted by two boys who came running toward him. They were Jacob Ruisdal's grandsons.

"Mr. Brevoort, Mr. Brevoort," they shouted. "Grandpa sent us to tell you that the surveyors are right near your home."

Old Brevoort rose quickly, his face full of anger and determination.

"Thank you, boys. Come later and I'll give you each a pear and an apple for the good news."

The boys ran off and Brevoort quickly went into the house. He came out just as quickly, holding an ancient blunderbuss in his hand.

"I'll show them how to run a road through my property," he growled to himself. Then he picked up a chair from the porch and carried it over near the gate. The view was such that he could see the field before him where there stood a beautiful elm tree.*

He sat down, put the gun over his knees, then took out his clay pipe and began smoking in thick, fast puffs. He must have sat there more than an hour, watching sharply all the time, when he heard men's voices. He

* He was looking at what is now Union Square.

quickly put away his pipe and took a firm hold of the
gun with both his hands, mumbling, "That's them. I'm
ready." Then he shut his lips tight and knitted his eyebrows.

There was silence for a time; then he heard the voices nearer. He rose and put the gun in the crook of his arm, keeping a sharp lookout.

Soon four men came in view and walked up to the gate.

"Who are you and what do you want?" Brevoort said harshly.

One of the men spoke: "We are the surveyors and engineers of the city and we are here to map out a street for the city through your farm. We'll also have to take some trees away."

"The *duyvil* you will! This is my land and I won't have any road going through it."

"Mr. Brevoort, these are orders from the government, and you must obey."

"The government cannot take any of my land without my permission, and I'm not giving my permission."

"You'll have to, and we are here to map out the street."

"You aren't going to map out anything here," said Brevoort.

The speaker turned to the other three: "Come on, men, we have the law on our side and we are going to map out the street."

"And I have my good shooting piece in my hand," said Hendrick, "and it's properly loaded. Anyone stepping on my land will be welcomed with a shot." He had raised the old gun to his shoulders, aiming at the standing men.

The way he held his gun and the determination in his voice showed that he meant what he said.

For a time they stood irresolute. Then the spokesman said: "Mr. Brevoort, you are defying the law, which, as a good citizen, you should not. We'll go now, but we'll come back and then you'll have to obey."

They walked away—but they did not return. Hendrick Brevoort had his way and no street went through his farm.

That is why, if you go to Broadway and Tenth Street, in New York City, where Grace Church stands today, you will see that Broadway turns off and goes along way up until it straightens out again.

10 The greatest hoax in New York City

Way back, in the horsey days, there lived an old wizened carpenter in New York City named Lozier. He was a little man, with a little white beard, but his blue eyes danced like leprechauns on a moonlit night and he was just chock-full of mischief. His best friend was old John de Voe, a butcher man, and he, too, was full of devilish pranks. Folks called him Uncle John. The horseplay these two made up in their heads was never written in books.

Both had worked hard for many years and had a few pennies in the bank, so they could sit on warm benches and figure out how to play tricks on their friends and neighbors.

On sunny days they and their cronies would get together in the Center Market, which was on the lower east side of New York City, and tell tales. There they settled how the world should be governed, and thought of new ways to make men laugh or show up their silly doings. There were plenty around with nothing to do but listen to tales of never-never land.

One afternoon Lozier and Uncle John were walking home.

"The city's been quiet a long time," said John.

"Aye, that's the truth, John," and Lozier shook his head and little beard up and down.

"We should be doin' somethin' to make a little noise. A good fire under the kettle sets the cover dancin'."

"You're always wantin' monkeyshines. Maybe you'd like to cut Manhattan Island in two, eh?"

"And why not, friend Lozier? That'd give the town somethin' t' crow 'bout."

"I was just wheezin' words out my head, Uncle John."

"Maybe you was, but it's a fine idea just the same," said John with a twinkle in his eye.

"Maybe, John. . . ." Then, slowly . . . "Just wait a minute! It's a fine idea. Cut Manhattan Island in two! There's a grand idea to make little fishes dance and laugh. . . . Ha! Cut the island in two if . . . It'd set folks on this here city dancin' the hoochy-koochy."

"What've you got in mind, Lozier?"

"John," said Lozier, grinning from ear to ear, "there's too many houses at one end of the island. It's top-heavy around the Battery. Somethin's got to be done about it."

"Y're a deep-thinkin' man, Lozier. Y're a deep-thinkin'

man," John said in the same tone. "What y're goin' t' do about it?"

"Aye, I'm thinkin' deep an' I got an idea!"

Then Lozier told Uncle John what was in his mind and what he was going to do, and they both held their sides with laughter.

"We'll carry it through, Lozier, sure as hens lay eggs. Folks minds is full o' fogs when they see money dangling before their noses."

The next day the two came to the market on Grand Street with long, solemn faces and sat down on a bench.

"What's wrong today?" asked a baker.

"Lots! Plenty! There's too many houses from here to the Battery," said Lozier in a gloomy voice.

"What's wrong with that?" said the candlestick maker.

"What's wrong with that, man! Where's your thinkin' pan? Can't you see the island might topple over right in the ocean? It's too heavy at one end." Lozier's voice was kind of sharp.

The word spread fast and men looked worried.

"We spoke to the mayor 'bout it," said John, offhand-like.

"Y' don't say!"

"Aye, so we did," said John slowly.

"I proposed a plan that 'd fix the whole business," said Lozier, raising his hand a little.

"Y' don' say! What's your plan?"

"Simple. Just saw off the island at the end where there's no buildin's, an' chain that end to the Battery side that's full o' houses. That'll put the heavy side in the middle instead of the end. The two empty parts of the island at each end 'll balance the heavy part."

There was silence all around. The thought was sinking in.

"That was Lozier's idea," said Uncle John, "and the mayor thought 'twas a fine proposition an' should be acted upon."

"Well," said Lozier slowly, "the mayor agreed with me."

"It'll be a big job and we'll need many men," said John.

"It's a mighty big job. We'll need many men an' we got 'em, an' we're goin' t' do it. The mayor put his red seal on it and asked me to start," spoke Lozier.

Start they did, Lozier and Uncle John. They began hiring men, who swallowed the tale hook, line, and sinker.

They hired men to do the sawing and the chaining and they hired carpenters to build barracks for the workers. They hired butchers to bring hogs and chickens, they hired farmers to bring potatoes and vegetables, and they hired cooks to cook and feed the workers.

Then they hired blacksmiths to make giant saws to cut the island in two and giant oars and locks to push the cut half around to the Battery side. And they spoke to ship supplies merchants about chains heavier than anchor chains to be used to fasten the cut part of the island to the other half.

All day long Center Market was a beehive around Lozier and Uncle John, who did all the bookkeeping, making ready to begin work.

It took many days, and men began asking, "When do we start? We can use the money."

"We'll start when all the preparations are done," the two said.

"We're ready," cried the butchers. "We're feeding fifty hogs, they'll make good meat, and we have no end o' crates full o' chickens."

"Just keep 'em ready until the proper time. We'll need 'em all when I give the big 'go ahead' word."

The men were clamoring more and more for the starting day and Lozier and John saw they could not hold back any longer. So they set a day for the ball to go a-

rolling. 'Twas to be an early Monday morning at the Bowery and Spring Street.

It had rained the night before and the day came sunny and glittering. Houses and cobblestone roads looked clean and shiny. So did the milling crowd of men, women, and children, full of high excitement.

There were butchers, bakers, and builders; there were workmen and carts and horses; there were food and fowl—everything all ready to start sawing Manhattan Island in two. The noise of the foot-loose crowd was loud to heaven. Men shouted, women chattered, children cried. But soon, almost all you could hear was: "Where's Lozier? Where's Uncle John?"

They looked here, they looked there, they looked everywhere—no Lozier, no Uncle John! They ran around and waited; they waited and they ran around. No sign of Uncle John or Lozier.

Questioning, crying, babbling all around, no answer . . . then it slowly sank into some folks' heads that the two had just played a joke on them—as they so often had done before.

There were cries and curses and roars of anger and revenge! Everyone was running around wildly looking for the two pranksters, but it did little good to cry "Giddap" when the horses were gone. No Uncle John or Lozier anyplace!

Now folks understood that a great fool-trick had been played on them. Some went home in wild anger at the two; others went home in red fury at themselves for being so blind and foolish, and some went home laughing at the blue monkeyshine Lozier and Uncle John had fed them. The sun warms the silly and the wise.

Since that time the tale is often told about the great hoax that was played on folks in New York City, who were not quick enough to see through two roguish fellows who liked laughing and pranking better than roasting and ragging.

11 Lucky star of Herald Square

Way, way back, there lived a Quaker boy, young Rowland Hussey Macy, on the island of Nantucket. Same as most boys of Nantucket, Rowland went to sea in a whaling boat to seek his fame and fortune.

For four long years he whaled and sailed on the whaler *Emily Morgan.* He ate fu-fu (corn meal and molasses) and salt horse (salted beef) and dandy-funk dish-pudding, and he helped catch whales as well. But when he came back he had no fame, and only a small sum of money, and a thick square beard. So he married a girl named Louise, and since her cooking was better than the whaling cook's salt horse and since he liked solid land better than heaving waves, he wouldn't go to sea again. Instead, he started his first thread and needle shop in Boston town.

Young Rowland Macy and his wife Louise worked long and hard—the honest way.

"We pay cash for what we buy. We owe money to no man. We must get cash for our goods," Rowland Macy and his wife Louise said.

But somehow the tidy shop did not thrive and soon Rowland and Louise had to give it up.

"I failed this first time, but I'll try again. Mine is an honest, Quaker way and I will succeed," Rowland Macy said.

"There is gold in California," said Louise and all her friends.

"Then we'll go to California and seek our fortune," Rowland agreed.

They went to California with thousands more to seek gold and riches.

When they got to the Yuba River, Rowland looked around for a time and then he said: "I have no mind for gold digging or gold panning. I'm a merchant man. I've tried once and now I'll try again."

So they opened a store on the Marysville River. But Quakers' ways were not for Western gold-rush towns, which were full of roughshod men and clever gamblers. So Rowland Macy and his wife gave up their second store and turned back home.

"I've had two shops and lost. I'll start a new one; maybe we'll have luck this time," spoke Rowland. So they

started the Haverhill Cheap Store in Haverhill, Massa-
chusetts.

> "We buy for C A S H
> We sell for C A S H
> We have only One Price!"

That's what Rowland Macy announced to the whole
world. It was his honest Quaker way.

Though he was a God-fearing man, like all men who
have lived at sea he believed in lucky signs, so he chose
a crowing rooster for good luck. He had one painted on
a board and hung it over his third store.

"The cock is the most famous of all the birds for
praising the Lord Jehovah, and he is the boldest as well.
As a rooster brings the hens to him, so will my shoppe
attract the ladies."

But even with Quaker honesty and with a rooster for
a lucky sign, Rowland Macy had no luck. Folks did not

like his simple way of selling. He lost his little business once again.

"I've failed three times, wife," said he to Louise, "but only the weak are beaten by ill-luck. For those who have no fear there is no defeat. I'll try again—a fourth time. I know I'll succeed. But now we'll go to great New York City and start a Fancy Dry Goods Shop there."

So he and Louise took the boat from Boston harbor to New York City. The winds blew wide, the clouds ran wild, the boat lurched up and down and deep and high. Captain and passengers had worried faces.

"If only I could see the stars to show me the course!" the captain said.

"Aye, the stars!" Rowland Macy mumbled in his beard.

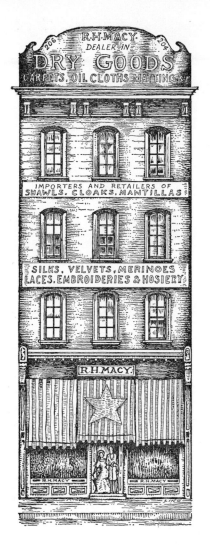

The boat leaped up high and sank deep, and fierce waves raced over the deck like wild horses.

Rowland stood silently near the shouting captain. He was silently praying to the Lord to help them in their plight. His eyes were turned heavenward to the racing clouds.

"Lord! Help us in Thy mercy!"

Then, like an answer to his prayer, there was a big rent in the black clouds, as if some hand had torn them apart and . . . there was a star, golden and gleaming, shining in the sky.

"See, there's a star to guide us!" cried the captain.

"So there is. The Lord in His mercy be thanked."

The boat was set on its proper course and in good time the vessel and passengers came safely into New York harbor.

Rowland Hussey Macy opened a new store—his fourth. For his trade-mark he took now the lucky sign of the star that had guided him safely into the harbor. A red-golden star!

The store under the sign of the red-golden star flourished like the cedars of Lebanon.

People came to buy in the honest Quaker way, and so it has kept on, until Macy's store with the red star was and is the biggest store in all New York City and in our land and in all the world.

12 The Irish luck of Brian Hughes

In the bygone golden days of New York City there lived a man named Brian Hughes, who was known and famous from New York to California for his humor and the jokes he played. He was ready for anything that would bring a good laugh and a little enjoyment.

You must know that in those days there were very few theaters, no movies, radios, or TV, and folks had to create their own entertainment. Jokes and hoaxes were of great amusement to everybody.

Brian Hughes was a rich man. He owned much land and was in the paper business besides. But his greatest pleasure, as I told you, was to play jokes on friends, strangers, and politicians.

Brian loved animals. A mongrel dog or an alley cat

was to him as good if not better than one with a fancy name and a long pedigree for which people paid a good deal of money.

One day he was sitting with friends in an eating place in the meat market discussing this very topic.

"You talk nonsense," said one redheaded fellow whose name was Esar. "A fine feline and a pedigreed dog are as different from their common kind as cats are from canaries." Mr. Esar always liked to use fancy words, and he was forever making up jokes with words.

"You talk that way, friend Esar, because everybody talks that way. I'll bet you dollars to doughnuts—no, I'll bet you a fine dinner at Rector's that if I put a common cat in a cat show, the high-toned judges wouldn't know the difference."

"That's just talk, people ain't such fools," said Maier, who was in the butcher business.

"No, people aren't fools, I know, but it's a cinch to fool 'em—most all the time, any time. All you got to do is just use a little sugar-coating and fancy icing."

"Hoi-poloi," from Maier.

"Well, I'll tell you what, Butch—and you, Esar—and you, Len (Leonard was a big, burly, genial builder man) —I'll bet you fellows three dinners at the town's three best restaurants: one at Delmonico's, one at Rector's, and one in the Plaza Hotel, that I can fool folks three times and it'll bring a good laugh to the whole city."

So Hoaxman Hughes, as his friends called him, and his three friends agreed on the bet—dinner in the finest three restaurants in New York City if he could fool folks with his funny games three times in succession. If he failed even once, he would have to treat all three friends to three meals in each of those expensive restaurants.

Now, Hoaxman Hughes had a smart head on his shoulders. He set his thinking machinery to work and soon he had his first plan ready.

One fine, sunny day he went to the City Hall where the members of the Board of Aldermen were sitting as usual in long-winded session. They were wagging their heads up and down and their tongues in every which way about laws that were of no value to any but themselves.

And because Brian Hughes was a big merchant who owned valuable land and houses, everyone treated him with great respect and listened to what he had to say. He spoke to the aldermen and they looked solemn and respectful.

"Honorable Aldermen," he said, "I want to donate to our fair city of New York a plot of land to be used as a public park for pleasure and for fun."

"We accept your very generous gift," the chairman of the Board said, "and we thank you for your great generosity. We will appoint a committee to look into the matter and make a report about it."

The committee was appointed, and the newspapers printed fine stories about Mr. Hughes's gift. For days the committee wrangled and argued about how the park was to be laid out. Then one committeeman, after discussing the matter with his wife, came back with the news that it was silly to argue about how to lay out the park when they had never seen the grounds. In a body, they went to examine the donated park grounds.

The site was a piece of land four feet by six feet! The aldermen looked at one another and all around, but it was still only a piece of ground scarcely large enough for a bench. They fumed and railed, but that did not change the size. In the end they went home saying many things about Hoaxman Hughes that I cannot tell you here.

So Brian Hughes had his first dinner, in Delmonico's fancy restaurant.

The day after the meal he again went into deep thought. He wanted his second dinner. He thought and he thought until he had the right thought.

I told you that Brian Hughes loved animals and now he remembered the argument that had started all the bets. He had claimed that alley cats and street dogs were as fine as any of fancy breed and that those who said they could tell one from the other were only tall-tale tellers from the timberland. He'd prove it.

He went down to the East Side and found some boys playing cops and robbers.

"I'll give a quarter for a fine alley cat," he said to them.

Before you could say Jack Sullivan they were off, and before you could say Jack Sullivan twice over they were back with a fine tiger alley cat.

Brian gave each and every boy a reward and they ran off, happier than boys at a picnic. Then Hughes set to work. He brushed and groomed and cleaned that **cat** without end. He fed her the finest food and she slept on soft cushions.

Two weeks later that alley cat looked as if she had come from a princess' palace. Sleek, soft, and shiny.

Like most alley cats, this one was mighty smart. She seemed to know what was expected of her. She walked proudly, head high in the air as if she belonged to **a** royal household.

Every year there was a great cat show in New York City. Only the rich and famous brought their cats, and there was a solemn jury of judges to decide which cat was the best.

Hoaxman Hughes entered his alley cat in the show.

Now, you know that when you enter a cat in one of these important shows, you must fill out long papers. You must tell who was the cat's father and mother and who were *their* fathers and mothers. Also, where the cat comes from and many more facts. Hughes said his cat's name was Nicodemus and that her ancestors were the famous Broomstick and Dustpan Sweeper.

Brian Hughes was always lucky—he called it his Irish luck. Nicodemus was given the First Prize as the best cat in the show.

The papers were full of the alley cat that was awarded first prize, and so Brian Hughes had his second great dinner, this time at Rector's.

"I've won two dinners and I must win the third. This time I must think of something even better," he said to his friends, "but my Irish luck will help me."

One day he went to the museum. He walked around looking at the beautiful paintings and statues that came from every part of the world and noticed that all the attendants were lolling around with nothing to do . . . and being paid for it.

"They should be doing something to earn their salaries—and that gives me a fine idea. Hallelujah! I'll get my third dinner."

He went down to Grand and Canal Streets and bought all the tools he could find that could be used to break into houses. When he came home, he went to his attic where he had some old picture frames lying around.

Then, in the middle of the night, Hughes, with a bag containing the tools and picture frames, came quietly up to the steps of the Metropolitan Museum, a big smile on his face. He threw tools and picture frames all over the steps and then—quietly went home. Not a soul had seen him.

The next morning there was a hue and cry throughout the city! Burglars had been in the museum! Someone must have surprised them, for they had dropped their tools and had fled. Some frames were found, but the paintings in them were gone! Which paintings had been stolen?

Every museum attendant was put to searching through every gallery to find what paintings were missing.

Hoaxman Hughes went to the museum. Every attendant was alert and watching. No one was lazing around. Hughes smiled.

"No money thrown away now!"

The next day he met his friends in the little restaurant on Fourteenth Street that was in the butchers' district.

"Well, Butch, Esar, and Len, I've earned my third dinner, and it must be in the Plaza Hotel."

"How come?" asked Maier.

Then Brian told them that the story they were reading in large black type in the newspapers about the museum robbery was just his own little joke—and he related exactly how he had planned it and carried it out.

"Well," said Leonard, "I've got to hand it to you."

"Nobody can play a joke on the whole city the way you do, Brian—not even I," added Esar.

"Friends," said Brian with a smile, "sometimes I think folks like to have a joke played on them so they can get a good laugh."

13 The clock must not stop

New York City was growing larger and larger. Thousands of new people came every month in big ships, and houses were spreading in all directions. Not only that, but builders were building houses higher all the time. These tall buildings were called cloud scrapers and skyscrapers, and folks liked to have their offices in these high skyscrapers.

One day the news spread that a new building, higher than any, would soon go up.

The great big New York Life Insurance Company would build the biggest, highest building in Manhattan —and that is just what the company did. It built a *nine-story* building on the corner of Liberty Street and Broadway! It was the biggest, highest structure from

Canal Street to the Battery. The directors of the company and the whole city were very proud of that wonderful building. And to make it even more wonderful, truly a show place, the directors ordered Henry Abbot, the most famous clock engineer of the city, to make the biggest four-dial clock that was ever made to be put into the building's top story. It was to be big enough to be seen from the Battery to Canal Street and from the Hudson River to the East River.

Mr. Abbot was a master clockmaker and so went to Boston and built the finest, biggest clock ever made for New York City—or any other place. The clock was put up in the top story of the new building, and it was the talk of the town. Truly, it was the marvel of the great metropolis. Folks actually could see it from the Battery to Canal Street and from the East River to the Hudson River.

The newspapers wrote no end of stories about this eighth wonder of the world, and the mayor of the city was proud of what the New York Life Insurance Company had done for the fame of New York.

For one day the clock worked perfectly, and men in the street set the time on their golden watches by that great clock. Then, the next day, something happened in the machinery of that unusual time piece and . . . the hands stopped moving!

Everyone in the office of the insurance company was frenzied. All the men in the nine stories went harum-scarum. The president of the company shouted orders for Henry Abbot to come at once, for he was the only man who could fix the clock.

Henry Abbot was a man prompt as the clocks he made, and in no time a carriage and two horses came dashing down Broadway to the skyscraper.

"Mr. Abbot," the president of the New York Life Insurance Company said sternly, "the clock you made for us at a very great cost has gone out of order the second day after it began to work. It must be fixed at once. My company cannot afford to and will not disappoint the people of this great city. We promised them they could tell the time by our clock from the Battery to Canal Street and from the Hudson River to the East River and *we will keep our promise!*" He pounded with his fist on the big mahogany table in his office.

"Mr. President," Mr. Abbot said, "I will examine the clock and I will repair it at once. I will return in fifteen minutes."

Mr. Abbot went out, and the president sat at his desk and waited. In ten minutes Abbot returned.

"Mr. President," he said, "the clock can be repaired, but I must take it to Boston where it was built, and it will take a maximum of four days to fix it."

"That cannot be, Mr. Abbot. My company promised the clock would be working from the day it was put up, and work it must! It is a question of the honor of my company, and the honor of my company must remain untarnished."

Henry Abbot knitted his brows, half closed his eyes,

and pursed his lips tight. Suddenly he opened his eyes wide and his brow smoothed out.

"Sir, I know how to solve this problem. The honor of your company will remain untarnished. Send for the superintendent of your building."

"I am here," spoke one of the men who was among the many who had crowded into the president's private office.

"Here is my watch, Mr. Superintendent." Abbot took his gold watch out of his vest pocket and took it off the heavy gold chain. "Here is my watch, which is absolutely accurate. Go up in the room behind the clock and hang it up where you have it in full sight all the time. Don't take your eyes off it. As the hands on my watch move, you move the hands of the giant clock from the back at exactly the same speed. Do it with perfect accuracy." Then, turning to the insurance company president, he said: "In this manner, sir, the people in the street will be able to tell the time. Thus you will keep your word and the honor of your company will remain without a blemish. I will take the machinery of the clock with me, and we shall work on it day and night and return it when it is done. I would also advise you, Mr. Superintendent, to get two or three men to take up your task when your hands get tired."

The president of the insurance company beamed with satisfaction.

"Mr. Abbot, you are as smart a man as you are a fine clock engineer. I am sure the superintendent is proud of the honor to move the hands of your clock. I will give him enough men to assist him in his noble task."

The works of the clock were carefully removed and taken to the factory, but the hands of the clock kept on moving, moving, telling all the citizens of New York City the exact time. Men stood by, day and night, moving the hands of the giant clock according to the hands of Mr. Abbot's watch.

Three days later the works were put back into the clock, and the men who had been moving the hands were relieved of their labor and given a fine reward.

Thus, everybody was happy: the city for having such a wonderful giant clock for all to see; the president of the insurance company for having upheld the honor of his organization, and the men who moved the hands for having done such a fine patriotic deed for the city they loved—New York.

14 The hope tree of Harlem

From the very early days, black folks lived together in the upper part of Manhattan Island that the first Dutch settlers called Haarlem. That was above what is now 125th Street.

With the years, more and more black folks came there, until they had a small city of their own. There were stores and restaurants and theaters, and every street just hummed with life like a beehive.

At 132nd Street and Seventh Avenue, which was part of Harlem, there was a fine theater called the Lafayette; it is now a church. It was named after the great French nobleman who helped the Americans in the Revolutionary War. Next to that theater was Connie's Inn, where all kinds of persons, many of them actors, often came to talk and argue and laugh. Outside, toward the middle of the road, stood a fine, big elm tree.

Those were the golden days of Negro actors, and most of them liked to come to Connie's Inn. When they grew tired of his hot, smoky place, they went outdoors to stand under the great shady elm. They stood around it and leaned against it, talking of their jobs and parts and telling jokes in friendly good humor. As these actors stood near the elm tree, the legend grew that it was a "Good Luck Tree"—that if you touched it or rubbed against it you'd have good luck in finding a job or succeeding in a part.

This belief spread all over Harlem and through the rest of the city. Folks believed in that "Hope Tree." Some laughed and said it was all silly chitter-chatter, but this made no difference. Folks like believing such things. Many who needed good luck came to the "Hope

Tree," or "Good Luck Tree," to rub against it and make their wish come true.

More and more people came to Harlem, crowding into its houses and streets, and the lawmakers who sit in City Hall making laws said the sidewalks of Seventh Avenue had to be widened so that folks wouldn't have to walk in the roads. This was dangerous and held up traffic. And the same was true of the Hope Tree. It, too, stood in the way of traffic and was a hazard. It would have to be destroyed—it stood in the way of progress.

The news of this went swiftly around all Harlem. Actors and everyone else were angry and dead-set against it. They had a meeting about it, and after long talks it was decided to choose a committee to go to see Bill Robinson, who was the "mayor" of Harlem and a mighty smart man. He could fix what needed fixing.

The committee went to his house and spoke:

"Bill Robinson, you are mayor of Harlem and we want you to save that Hope Tree. They're gonna tear it out."

"I'll go to see the 'Little Flower' "—that's what they called the big mayor down in City Hall—"and tell him what you said, that you don't want that Hope Tree torn out of the earth."

Bill Robinson and the committee went to see Mayor Fiorello La Guardia, the Little Flower, in City Hall. He was a little, round fellow with an honest face and dancing eyes, sitting in a chair before his big desk.

"Your Honor," Bill Robinson said, "folks up in Harlem don't want the Hope Tree growing on 132nd Street and Seventh Avenue torn out. Actors and other folks, too, say it brings them luck and makes wishes come true."

"Folks are always right," the Little Flower said. "But what are we gonna do about progress, about folks walking on the streets, and about the traffic? The sidewalks aren't wide enough, and it's dangerous to walk in the streets. That tree makes plenty of trouble for traffic." Then he was quiet for a time, head down, thinking. Suddenly he looked up with a smile. "I'll tell you what: I'm gonna plant a fine new elm tree where it won't interfere with anybody walking or riding. It won't get in anybody's way and everybody will be happy."

Bill Robinson went back to Harlem and told folks what the big mayor at City Hall had decided.

Some said it was okay. Some didn't like it.

"The new tree'll never be like the good old Hope Tree."

But the law is the law, and a day was set for the tree to be taken out and the new tree planted.

Talk ran high all over Harlem. Crowds came to touch the tree for the last time. Then one smart merchant began chopping off branches, cutting them into splinters and selling them to keep for good luck—and he sold them very cheaply. Everybody was buying those chips. So he chopped off most all of the branches and splintered them and folks bought and bought. They put them in their pocketbooks and in their lockets, they put them on strings and wore them around their necks, and they put them in their hats—all for good luck.

Bill Robinson took home a big twig and even those who didn't believe in such things bought the chips anyway. Maybe. . . .

So the tree was taken away, but the smart owner of the Apollo Theater, wise Mr. Schiffman with the bright blue eyes, took a big part of the trunk of that tree into the theater. There he set it in the wings, and on Amateur Night, when the new talents tried their stunts and songs for the first time before the audience, they'd touch the tree before going on the stage to make sure they'd get a job and not the hook.

Soon the big day came when the new Hope Tree was to be planted.

The Little Flower, bustling Mayor La Guardia of City Hall, came. He wore baggy trousers and a wide-brimmed hat, one he always wore, and he had a big smile on his face. Bill Robinson was there too, with a high black silk hat and a friendly face. Thousands were on hand to help plant the new Hope Tree. There were grand speeches and cheering, and the mayor said he, too, had touched the Hope Tree, and he hoped it would bring him good luck. Everybody cheered, even though some said it was just politics.

Then he said he'd set what was left of the stump of the old tree in concrete so it would last forever. Everybody cheered and shouted.

And that was just what was done. The stump was set in concrete and a low metal fence was set around it that you can see to this very day.

And to this day you will find folks who have a chip

of the Hope Tree. They give it to young ones they love, to keep for good luck, even as it has brought them good luck through the years.

Notes about the stories

• *The tale of the three footsteps*

The lore of footsteps and footprints is very extensive and is connected with many beliefs and tales—much magic is attached to footprints left in ashes, on the ground, on stones, etc.

Tales of footprints left in rocks and on mountains, whether they be of the Devil or of heroes, are common throughout the world. That the steps here attributed to the Devil are connected with the Indians is interesting but not unusual in North America. Indians and devils were considered in the same realm—a concept that shows unquestionable European influence. Such footprint folktales are found all over the United States and generally are connected with impressions on rocks that resemble the sole of a foot.

This particular story is well known and told often all along

Long Island, Westchester, and Connecticut, where many rocks and boulders are found.

• *The ghost of Peg-Leg Peter*

The tale of the ghost of Peter Stuyvesant is one of the classic narratives of the fearless peg-leg governor. I have spent a great deal of time, for many years, around the Church of St. Marks on the Bouwerie, where the old governor is buried. Many of the heads of the church have been my friends, and tales of those buried there are forever cropping up. Those of the testy, fearless Peg-Leg Peter are always in the fore. I have heard this particular story countless times.

• *The courageous Quaker of Flushing*

Although the tale of John Bowne is factual and is known all around Long Island and wherever there are Quakers, it has been told so many times, for so many years, that it can well be put into the realm of folktales. Surely a folktale should preserve the story of a courageous and honest man.

You will hear this story whenever Quakers tell tales—even as I heard it.

• *How the duyvil gave New Amsterdam to the English*

The name "Spuyten Duyvil" is still mentioned to this very day by millions of New Yorkers, for it is a small body of water at the northern end of Manhattan Island that millions cross daily. How it got its name is one of the classic tales of our Dutch period.

Battles between the Devil and humans is a favorite European folk theme and was brought to America when white immigrants first began to come here.

Who told it to me first? I don't remember. I have known the story ever since my childhood, when I came to the United States.

• *Clever Mistress Murray*

Folktales often blossom richly in dried and harsh history. When such history is mellowed by a thousand-times telling, it becomes a folktale. Such is the tale of Mrs. Robert Murray, who saved four thousand American patriots from capture by the English Redcoats. This story has been blooming as an historical folktale for near three hundred years.

There is a famous painting of the scene of Mistress Murray and the British High Command in the New York Historical Society building.

I have known the story for many years.

• *The phantom fire ship*

One of the most popular types of folktale—ghost stories—deals with ships and the sea. I don't believe there is a harbor in the world that does not have its own ghost tale of a ship or crew, and so, naturally, has Long Island.

The tale of a burning object that does not disintegrate into ashes is a theme handed down from Biblical times. Only then it was a burning bush.

The story of the ever-burning ship is well known along the Sound and comes up whenever sea stories are told. I have heard it more than once.

• *Commodore Vanderbilt's first boat*

A few of the great American millionaires, the empire builders of our country, caught the popular fancy of the people, and Cornelius Vanderbilt is one of them. Tales about him keep on growing. If you spend any afternoon or evening in one of the good clubs of New York City you will find men sitting in deep-cushioned armchairs leisurely telling tales of bygone days and bygone men—Vanderbilt among them.

But this story I did not hear in a high-ceilinged club lobby—I heard it, among many others, from a friend since gone, Owen D. Shepherd, once an important official of the International Paper Company. He had heard many tales from friends and enjoyed telling them. This particular story was one of the Commodore's own favorites, one he himself enjoyed telling to his friends.

• *"Mornin', Mighty Mose"*

The story of "Mighty" or "Big" Mose is a very interesting one. If memory serves me well I first heard about him in 1907, when I spent a good deal of time around Rivington Street and the Bowery. One of the "fellows" I knew was called "Niggie." Though he was no more than seventeen, he was very friendly with gangsters and Tammany heelers. I remember distinctly being admonished by him now and then not to be a "Big Mose." Every once in a while a story would crop up about the fireman fighter.

Many years later, when Herbert Asbury, that indefatigable researcher of men and cities, was a patient of mine, we often discussed Big Mose. The story told here is one of the many I heard about the New York City Superman.

The Mighty Mose tall tales are typical American tales that flourish more in our land than in any other.

I don't remember just who first told it to me, so often have I heard it repeated.

• *The bloodless battle of the elm*

Hendrick Brevoort was a doughty Dutchman of the old school. At ninety-four, he frightened off the New York City surveyors from his farm and that is why Broadway turns off at Tenth Street instead of running parallel with the other avenues.

This particular tale belongs to the group of Dutch stories that are part and parcel of our Dutch heritage. I really don't remember when I first heard or read it, but I have listened to it being told so many times since at Historical Society meetings that it needs no particular informant.

• *The greatest hoax in New York City*

The district that takes in Eleventh, Twelfth, Thirteenth, and Fourteenth Streets at the extreme west end near the Hudson River is the great meat center of New York City. If you lunch there often, where butchermen eat, you are sure of good food, and if you become acquainted with these men you are apt to hear good New York stories. It was there I heard this tale among many others.

The sawing apart of Manhattan Island to prevent it from sinking into the ocean is one of the classic New York City folktales.

The facts actually took place and are almost beyond fantasy. I think it would be difficult even for Professor Stith Thompson, the great fountainhead of folktale studies of the world, to find a parallel to these facts. The story is told whenever and wherever tales of Old New York are told and therefore belongs in this book.

• *Lucky star of Herald Square*

There is not a country in the world where "Macy's" is not known. It is truly an institution rather than a store, and it is, in fact, a living saga.

The story of the Quaker couple who started the store and their determination to live up to the mottoes that honesty is the best policy, and that an object bought should be paid for at once is a tale worth telling. How they chose a star as their symbol is really in the realm of folklore. It is told from New England to California and up and down the land as well.

Where did I hear it? First in Cape Cod, in New England, then in California, and finally in New York City.

• *The Irish luck of Brian Hughes*

This is another of the stories I heard in the meat market. Years ago I lived in Greenwich Village and almost every week I would go to a small restaurant on Fourteenth Street and Eleventh Avenue, to which many meat merchants came to eat. I went there on Fridays for an excellent clam chowder and other unsurpassed dishes, and there I became acquainted with many of these merchants. From them I heard many tales, this among others.

There are innumerable stories told of Brian Hughes, as I

learned on inquiring at the Dollar Bank of New York, of which Mr. Hughes was one of the first presidents.

Mr. William Gebracht, assistant vice-president of the bank now, whose father knew Mr. Hughes, added some tales he had heard from his father.

Mr. Murdy of the same bank was also helpful with my research work.

• *The clock must not stop*

I cannot think of a more pleasing story of New York's mug-and-mustache age than that of the famous first "skyscraper" and how the clock was made to move. I first heard the story first in the Green Room Club. The officers in charge of the archives of the New York Life Insurance Company were of great help to me in authenticating the tale.

• *The hope tree of Harlem*

The tale of the Hope Tree is a living legend in New York City. You can see the trunk imbedded in concrete on 132nd Street and Seventh Avenue, right in the center of Manhattan. And you can read the inscription on the bronze plaque:

TREE OF HOPE
BELOVED BY THE PEOPLE OF HARLEM.
YOU ASKED FOR A TREE OF HOPE
SO HERE 'TIS. BEST WISHES
BILL ROBINSON

The elm tree stood there near the Lafayette Theater, which is now the Methodist Episcopal Church.

I have known the story for years, but Mr. Frank Schiffman, a theater man for many, many years who ran the Lafayette Theater and now directs the Apollo Theater in Harlem, refreshed my memory and added many interesting details. It was Mr. Schiffman who took a large part of the trunk of the tree to the Lafayette Theater when the tree was cut down.

In that theater they had amateur nights. The trunk of the tree was placed in the wings, and every amateur actor, singer, or acrobat would touch that trunk for good luck before going onstage.

Then, when Mr. Schiffman took over the Apollo Theater, the tree trunk was put into storage. It turned up—of all places—a few miles from my farm in Carmel! The story appeared in the local paper and is worth reprinting:

"At the time of the Mahopac Falls firemen's fair Maurice L. Condon of Mahopac was searching for a place to park when he noticed a tree trunk which seemed somehow familiar. Mr. Condon was amazed to find that it really was the old wishing tree of Harlem, which he had helped to replace about ten years ago. The original tree had been literally plucked to death by folks anxious to have their wishes come true and Mr. Condon was in charge of the job of replacing it for the New York City Park Department. The tree was located for many years near Seventh Avenue in Harlem.

"The inscription on the plaque which was set into the old tree when it was replaced reads: 'The original wishing tree beloved by the people of Harlem. According to Harlem legend anyone who touches this tree and makes a wish will have that wish fulfilled.' The original tree is an American elm and that was replaced by an oak.

"Inquiry by The Press as to what eventually happened to the original wishing tree revealed that it was finally dumped and a concrete replica erected in Harlem. However, no one knows who reclaimed the original wishing tree from the dump, or when and why it was brought to Mahopac Falls. But there it is and if you wish to prove it all you need do is touch the tree and make a wish. According to legend your wish will be fulfilled."

I have been trying to find the trunk of the tree, but so far I have had no luck.

Some songs of old New York

And now that you have read the stories of old New York City, you might like to learn a few of the songs of old New York.

You may want just to read them, or sing them, or play them, or play and sing them.

The songs are in a small way related to the stories. I have heard them sung many a time, and I have sung them as well. Now you try, and I am sure it will be as much fun and bring as much pleasure to you as it did to me.

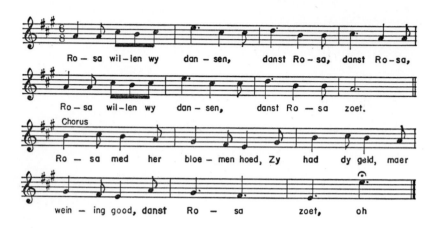

1. *Rosa, willen wy dansen, danst Rosa, danst Rosa,*
   Rosa, willen wy dansen, danst Rosa zoet.

       Rosa med her bloemenhoed,
       Zy had dy geld, maer weining good,
       Danst Rosa zoet, oh.

2. *Rosa willen wy minnin, mint Rosa, mint Rosa,*
   Rosa willen wy minnin, mint Rosa zoet.
       (Chorus)

3. *Rosa willen wy trouwen, tro trouwen, tro trouwen,*
   Rosa willen wy trouwen, trout Rosa zoet.
       (Chorus)

1. Rosa, will you be dancing, O Rosa, my Rosa,
   Rosa, will you be dancing, O Rosa sweet.

   > Rosa with her hat of flowers,
   > Has little wealth but happy hours,
   > And dances sweetly.

2. Rosa, will you be mine now, O Rosa, my Rosa,
   Rosa, will you be mine now, O Rosa sweet.
   > (*Chorus*)

3. Rosa will you be married, O Rosa, my Rosa,
   Rosa will you be married, O Rosa sweet.
   > (*Chorus*)

1. Of all the girls that are so smart
   There's none like pretty Sally,
   She is the darling of my heart,
   And she lives in our alley.
   There's ne'er a lady in the land
   That's half so sweet as Sally,
   For she's the darling of my heart,
   And she lives in our alley.

2. Her father he makes cabbage nets
   For those that want to buy 'em;
   Her mother she makes laces long
   And thro' the streets does cry 'em.
   But sure such folks could ne'er beget
   So sweet a girl as Sally;
   She is the darling of my heart
   And she lives in our alley.

3. When she is by I leave my work,
   I love her so sincerely.
   My master comes like any Turk
   And bangs me most severely.
   But let him bang his belly full,
   I'll bear it all for Sally,
   For she's the daring of my soul,
   And she lives in our alley.

4. Of all the days into the week
   I dearly love but one day,
   And that's the day that comes between
   A Saturday and Monday.
   For then I'm drest in all my best
   To walk abroad with Sally;
   For she's the darling of my soul,
   And she lives in our alley.

NEW YORK, OH, WHAT A CHARMING CITY

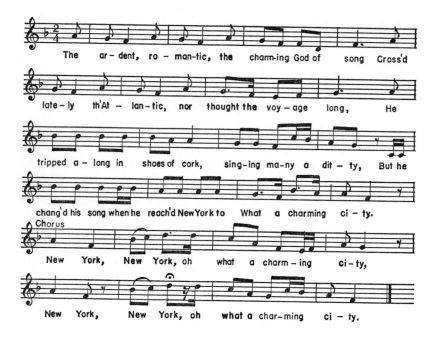

1. The ardent, romantic, the charming God of song
   Cross'd lately th'Atlantic, nor thought the voyage long,
   He tripped along in shoes of cork, singing many a ditty,
   But he chang'd his song when he reach'd New York
   To What a Charming City

      New York, New York, oh, what a charming city,
      New York, New York, oh, what a charming city.

2. In Bowery, in Broadway, he rambled up and down,
   Took by-way and odd-way, resolved to see the town,
   And as he went he sang this song, Now is it not a pity
   I should have stayed away so long from such a charming City.

      New York, New York, oh, what a charming city,
      New York, New York, oh, what a charming city.

3. Here freedom and duty and truth and taste remain,
   Here honor and beauty and love and valor reign,
   Then hither Freedom's friends resort, the grave, the gay, the
      witty,
   For here I'll henceforth keep my court in this delightful city.

      New York, New York, oh, what a charming city,
      New York, New York, oh, what a charming city.

1. Now ladies and gentlemen, how do you do?
   I come out before you with one boot and one shoe,
   I don't know how 'tis, but somehow 'tis so.
   Now isn't it hard upon Billy Barlow.

   > O dear raggedy O
   > Now isn't it hard upon Billy Barlow.

2. Do show me a boarding house where I can stay,
   I'm so hungry and sleepy, I've eat nothing today,
   They'll not let me in at Astor's, I know,
   But a market stall's vacant for Billy Barlow.
   > (*Chorus*)

3. As I went down the street the other fine day,
   I met two fair ladies, just coming this way;
   Says one—now that chap, he isn't so slow;
   I guess not, says the other, that's Mr. Barlow.
       (*Chorus*)

4. I'm told there's a show coming into town,
   Red lions and monkeys and porcupines brown;
   But if they should show I shall beat them, I know,
   For they've never a varmint like Billy Barlow.
       (*Chorus*)

5. I went to the races on Long Island so gay,
   The man at the gate then he ask'd me to pay,
   What pay, Sir, says I, and I look'd at him so;
   Pass on, Sir, I know you, you're Mr. Barlow.
       (*Chorus*)

6. I had been on the track but a minute or two,
   When the people flock'd round me, what I tell you is true;
   Who's that little fat gentleman, does anyone know?
   Yes, says a young lady, that's Mr. Barlow.
       (*Chorus*)

7. O dear, but I'm tired of this kind of life,
   I wish in my soul I could find a good wife;
   If there's any Young Lady in want of a beau,
   Let her fly to the arms of sweet Billy Barlow.
       (*Chorus*)

8. Now, ladies and gemmen, I bid you goodby;
   I'll buy a new suit when clothes ain't so high;
   My hat's shocking bad, as all of you know,
   But looks well on the head of Billy Barlow.
       (*Chorus*)

WALKING DOWN BROADWAY

The sweet-est thing in life (and no one dare say nay),____ on a
Sat-ur-day af-ter noon is walk-ing down Broad-way,____ My
sis-ters in the park or at Long Branch wish to stray, But
I pre-fer to walk down the fes — tive gay Broad — way.____

Chorus

Walk-ing down Broad-way,____ the fes-tive gay Broad-way, The
Okay thing on Sat — ur — day is walk-ing down Broad-way,____
Walk-ing down Broad-way, the fes — tive gay Broad—way, The
Okay thing on Sat — ur — day is walk-ing down Broad — way.

1. The sweetest thing in life (and no one dare say nay),
   On a Saturday afternoon, is walking down Broadway,
   My sisters in the park or at Long Branch wish to stray,
   But I prefer to walk down the festive gay Broadway.

   > Walking down Broadway, the festive gay Broadway,
   > The okay thing on Saturday is walking down Broadway,
   > Walking down Broadway, the Festive gay Broadway,
   > The okay thing on Saturday is walking down Broadway.

2. Last Wednesday afternoon my cousin Will did say,
   "Nellie, come along with me, I'll take you down Broadway—
   To the theater Comique to see Captain Jinks so gay,
   Then we'll dine at Delmonico's 'fore returning down Broadway.

   > Walking down Broadway, the festive gay Broadway,
   > The okay thing on Saturday is walking down Broadway,
   > Walking down Broadway, the Festive gay Broadway,
   > The okay thing on Saturday is walking down Broadway.